S0-CFE-335

F. Dotzauer

VIOLONCELLO
METHOD
VOLUME I

(English, French and German Text)

Revised and Amplified by
Johannes Klingenberg

Published in Two Volumes
Volume 1 (O3674)
Volume 2 (O3675)

CARL FISCHER®

O3674

65 Bleecker Street, New York, NY 10012

ISBN 978-0-8258-0940-7

Reissued in 1951
by Carl Fischer, Inc., New York

Preface

While none of the Dotzauer methods has proved serviceable for modern requirements in their original versions, the excellence of the material contained therein has induced me to select and edit that which has remained of the greatest serviceability for present-day needs and combine it in the present method.

Much of the unnecessary material has been omitted and replaced by suitable selections from the works of B. Romberg, J. L. Duport and J. B. Gross and the whole has been systematized and arranged in such progressive order as to insure the speediest and most satisfactory advancement of the student.

From the very start, the pupil's attention must be called incessantly to the importance of gaining surety in the playing of major and minor thirds, the entire technic of the 'cello being based in a measure upon the differences of these intervals.

The purpose of this method is to provide a complete and thorough course of instruction based upon the fundamental principles of 'cello playing and with the aid of the necessary talent and application, the material offered cannot fail but enable the student to arrive at and master many of the higher accomplishments of his art.

Vorwort

Keine der Dotzauer'schen Schulen schien nach dem heutigen Stande des Violoncell-Unterrichtes zu unverändertem Wiederabdruck geeignet, aber die Güte und Verwendbarkeit des in ihnen enthaltenen Lehrstoffes veranlasste mich, denselben in vorliegender Schule von neuem möglichst nutzbringend anzuordnen und zu gestalten. Zur Ausfüllung der vorhandenen Lücken wurden teilweise ältere, oft bewährte Beispiele von B. Romberg, J. L. Duport und J. B. Gross gewählt und für das Ganze eine systematisch fortschreitende und übersichtliche Anordnung erstrebt, die allein dem Schüler ein sicheres und schnelles Vorwärtsschreiten ermöglicht. Der Lehrer versäume nicht, den Schüler im mühelosen Erkennen der grossen und kleinen Terzen zu üben, denn auf dem Unterschiede dieser beiden Intervalle beruht die Violoncell-Technik zumeist.

Zweck der Schule möge sein, dem angehenden Violoncellisten eine sichere und manierenfreie Grundlage zu bieten, von der ausgehend es ihm bei Talent und dem nötigen Fleisse gelingen kann auch höhere Staffeln in der Kunst des Violoncell-Spiels zu erreichen.

Préface

Aucune des diverses Méthodes de Violoncelle de Dotzauer ne semblait pouvoir supporter l'épreuve de la réédition, étant donné le niveau élevé qu'atteint aujourd'hui l'étude de cet instrument. Et cependant l'excellence pratique des exercices qu'elle contient m'a déterminé à la remettre au jour, en l'utilisant de la façon la plus profitable à l'élève. J'ai comblé les lacunes qu'elle présentait par des exemples choisis de B. Romberg, J. L. Duport et J. B. Gross, et je me suis efforcé de grouper ces différents éléments dans un ordre systématique et progressif, de façon à former un ensemble qui fasse faire à l'élève des progrés rapides et sûrs. Le professeur devrá de bonne heure éxercer l'élève à distinguer les tierces majeures et mineures, car la technique du Violoncelle repose en bonne partie sur la différence entre ces deux intervalles.

Le but de cétte méthode est donc d'offrir aux commençants une base d'études, nouvelle dans sa forme et éprouvée dans ses éléments, qui, le travail aidant, les conduira rapidement à la virtuosité.

Johannes Klingenberg

The Violoncello,

which was developed from the former Bass-Viol, was first constructed in the 17th century, and is the instrument which most resembles the human voice, both in quality and expression.

The holding of the instrument.

The pupil must sit on the border of the chair, advance the left foot a little and draw back the right one; the Violoncello is held by means of the legs, that is, in such a manner that the lower edge of the back of the instrument touches the left leg, and the upper edge of the back must lean easily against the body of the player. When using the tail-pin of the instrument, it is necessary to have it so long, that the lowest peg reaches the left ear at about two or three inches distance, so as not to run the risk of striking the left knee with the bow while bowing upon the A string. (Fig. I)

The guiding of the bow.

The bow is to be held by the right hand, in such a manner that the tip of the thumb is placed sideways against the corner of the nut; the forefinger must be placed in such a manner as to press the stick with the upperjoint; the tip of the middle finger must touch the hair and the other fingers take an easy and natural position adjoining the nut. For the down-bow, that is, starting from the nut of the bow, the wrist of the right hand is to be held a little upwards, the elbows and the point of the bow must be lowered and the bow must be drawn across the strings at about three inches from the bridge, whilst the wrist is gradually descending. For the up-bow, that is, starting from the point, the wrist must be raised gradually, so that the bow crosses the strings in a straight line. The hair of the bow in passing over the A, D & G string, is to lean sideways towards the bridge, but on the C string the bow is to be held in such a manner that the full breadth of the hair lies flatly on the strings. (Fig. IVa and IVb.)

The tuning of the Violoncello.

This instrument is tuned in fifths:

in beginning to learn it, it is advisable to tune to the Piano or some other well-tuned instrument by giving the above mentioned notes; when turning the pegs, one ought to press them as far into the peg-box as possible, as they are apt to slip. (Fig. IIa & IIb.)

20501

Das Violoncell,

eine Umgestaltung der früheren Gamba, ist im Anfange des 17. Jahrhunderts aufgekommen. Es ist dasjenige Instrument, welches der menschlichen Stimme am nächsten verwandt und des höchsten Ausdruckes fähig ist.

Haltung des Instrumentes.

Der Spieler setze sich auf den vorderen Teil des Stuhles, strecke den linken Fuss ein wenig aus und setze den rechten Fuss weiter zurück. Das Instrument wird mit den Beinen so gehalten, dass der untere Rand des Bodens an das linke und der untere Rand des Deckels an das rechte Bein zu liegen kommt; der obere Rand des Bodens lehnt sich ganz leicht an den Körper. Wendet man einen Stift (Stachel) an, so wähle man diesen so hoch, dass der unterste Wirbel in gleicher Linie, etwa ein paar cm. vom linken Ohr entfernt ist und man nicht beim Anstreichen der A-Saite Gefahr läuft, an das linke Knie zu stossen. (Fig. I)

Von der Führung des Bogens.

Der Bogen wird mit der rechten Hand so gefasst, dass die Daumenspitze ein wenig seitwärts an die Spitze des Frosches zu liegen kommt, der Zeigefinger so weit vorrückt, dass er mit der Biegung seines obersten Gelenkes auf die Bogenstange, der Mittelfinger mit der Spitze an die Haare und die zwei übrigen Finger ungezwungen an den Frosch und die Stange zu liegen kommen. Der Bogen wird auf der A, D und G-Saite so zum Strich angesetzt, dass die Haarfläche dem Stege zugekehrt erscheint; die C-Saite jedoch muss mit der ganzen Haarfläche angestrichen werden. Beim Herunterstrich (d. h. vom Frosche zur Spitze gezogen) biege man das rechte Handgelenk ein wenig, senke den Ellbogen und auch die Spitze des Bogens ein wenig, führe den Bogen etwa 3 cm. vom Stege entfernt über die Saiten und lasse das Handgelenk langsam einsinken. Im Hinaufstrich (d. h. von der Spitze zum Frosche gezogen) hebe man das Handgelenk nach und nach, damit der Bogen die Saite immer gerade durchschneidet.

Von der Stimmung des Violoncells.

Das Instrument wird in Quinten:

gestimmt. Anfangs stimme man womöglich nach dem Klavier oder nach einem anderen Instrument ein, indem man sich oben bezeichnete Töne angibt. Beim Umdrehen der Wirbel übe man einen festen Druck gegen den Wirbelkasten aus, damit der Wirbel nicht herunterschnellt. (Fig. IIa u. IIb.)

Le Violoncelle,

qui est une transformation de la ci-devant Gambe, fut construit au 17me siècle; c'est l'instrument qui ressemble le plus à la voix humaine et qui possède les qualités nécessaires pour exprimer le mieux les différentes dispositions de l'âme en touchant le coeur par des sons doux et mélodieux.

Position du corps pour tenir l'instrument.

Il faut que l'élève soit assis sur le bord de la chaise, qu'il étende un peu le pied gauche et qu'il retire le pied droit. L'instrument doit être placé entre les jambes, de manière que le bord inférieur du fond touche la jambe gauche, le bord inférieur de la table la jambe droite. Le bord supérieur du fond doit toucher légèrement le corps. Quand on se sert du ferret (goupille), il faut qu'il soit d'une longuer, afin que la cheville la plus basse soit à la hauteur et éloignée à peu près de 2 cm. de l'oreille gauche, pour éviter de pousser contre le genou gauche en touchant la corde de LA. (Fig. I)

Manière de tenir l'archet.

On tient l'archet par la main droite afin que le bout du pouce s'incline un peu du côté vers le coin de la hausse, l'index doit s'avancer de manière que la jointure de dessus se place sur la baguette et que le bout du doigt du milieu touche les crins de l'archet, les deux autres doigts doivent se mettre en même temps légèrement sur la hausse et la baguette. En tirant l'archet, c'est à dire, commençant au talon, il faut qu'on tienne le poignet un peu élevé, le coude abaissé ainsi que la pointe de l'archet, qu'on même à travers les cordes, éloigné à peu près de 3 cm. du chevalet en observant que le poignet s'incline peu à peu. En poussant l'archet, c'est à dire, commençant à la pointe, il faut relever le poignet peu à peu, pour que l'archet, en passant sur les cordes, soit en rectangle avec ces dernières. Les crins de l'archet doivent s'incliner vers le chevalet sur la corde de LA, RÉ et SOL, mais sur la corde de l'UT la tenue de l'archet doit être telle que les crins se trouvent justement au dessus de la baguette. (Fig. IVa & IVb.)

De l'accord du Violoncelle.

On accorde le Violoncelle en Quintes:

Au commencement on fera mieux d'accorder d'après le Piano ou de quelque autre instrument en touchant les notes ci-devant nommées. En tournant les chevilles, pressez la main contre la tête de l'instrument pour éviter que les chevilles ne glissent en arrière. (Fig. IIa & IIb.)

FIG. I.

The Violoncello and how it is held; showing correct position of the left hand, position of right arm while bowing at tip and nut of bow, as well as general attitude of player.

Das Violoncello und seine richtige Haltung; correcte Position der linken Hand, richtige Führung des rechten Armes am Frosch und an der Spitze des Bogens, sowohl wie allgemeine richtige Position des Spielers.

Le violoncelle et la manière de tenir l'instrument; position exacte de la main gauche; direction à suivre pour le bras droit, suivant que l'archer est pris au talon ou à la pointe; tenue genérale du violoncelliste.

FIG. II a.

Position of the Fingers of the left Hand. | Die Haltung der Finger der linken Hand. | Position des doigts de la main gauche.
(Close Position.) | (Enge Lage.) | (Position normale.)

FIG. II b.

Position of the Fingers of the left Hand. | Die Haltung der Finger der linken Hand. | Position des doigts de la main gauche.
(Extended Position.) | (Weite Lage.) | (Position écartée.)

FIG. III b.

The Thumb Position on | Der Daumeneinsatz auf | Position du pouce sur
the two lower strings. | den beiden tieferen Saiten | le sol et l'ut. (Voir page
(See page 92.) | (Siehe Seite 92.) | 92.)

FIG. III a.

The Thumb Position on | Der Daumeneinsatz auf | Position du pouce sur
the two upper Strings. | den beiden oberen Saiten. | le la et le ré. (Voir page
(See page 92.) | (Siehe Seite 92.) | 92.)

FIG. IV a.

Correct manner of hol- | Die richtige Haltung | Manière de tenir l'ar-
ding the bow. (Position | des Bogens. (Position | chet. (Position exacte des
of the fingers and thumb.) | der Finger und des Daumens) | doigts et du pouce.)

FIG. IV b.

Correct manner of hol- | Die richtige Haltung | Manière de tenir l'ar-
ding the bow. (Outer view | des Bogens. (Aeussere | chet. (Aspect extérieur
of the hand and wrist.) | Ansicht der Hand und | de la main et du poignet.)
| des Gelenkes). |

The position of the left hand.

The left hand leans against the neck of the instrument, so that the thumb in the first positions rests on the back of the neck opposite the fore and middle finger; the fingers must be in an upright position and are to fall with the utmost strength and precision on the strings. The left arm maintains an easy attitude

Name of the parts of the Violoncello and of the bow.

1. The top and on the opposite side the back.
2. The ribs.
3. The F holes.
4. The tail-pin.
5. The tail-piece.
6. The finger board.
7. The neck.
8. The saddle.
9. The peg.
10. The peg-box.
11. The scroll.
12. The bridge.
13. The bow-stick.
14. The head or tip.
15. The nut or frog.
16. The hair.

Benennung der Teile des Violoncells und des Bogens.

1. *Die Decke und gegenüber der Boden.*
2. *Die Zargen.*
3. *Die F-Löcher.*
4. *Der Stiften oder Stachel.*
5. *Der Saitenhalter.*
6. *Das Griffbrett.*
7. *Der Hals.*
8. *Der Sattel.*

For those who are interested in the history of the Violoncello "The History of the Violoncello by J. W. v. Wasielewski": can be recommended.

The rudiments of music, necessary for learning the violoncello.

The five lines employed in the notation as used at present are designated as the staff.

The notes in the Bass-clef 𝄢: are called:

Von der Haltung der linken Hand.

Die linke Hand legt sich so an den Hals des Instrumentes, dass der Daumen in den ersten Lagen an der hinteren Seite ungefähr gegenüber der Mitte des 1. und 2. Fingers ruht. Die Finger müssen gleichsam wie Hämmer auf die Saiten fallen. Der linke Arm behält eine ungezwungene Haltung.

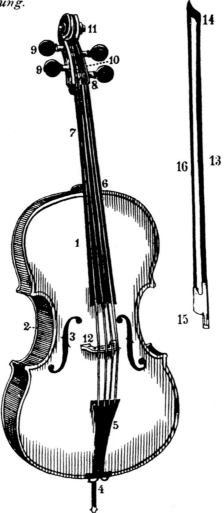

Violoncello.

Wer sich für den Entwicklungsgang des Violoncells interessiert, dem möge das Werk „Geschichte des Violoncells von J. W. von Wasielewski" bestens empfohlen sein.

Kurzgefasste für den Violoncellunterricht notwendige Elementar-Musiklehre.

Die fünf Linien in der Notenschrift nennt man Notensystem.

Die Noten heissen im Bassschlüssel 𝄢:

De la tenue de la main gauche.

La main gauche doit se placer au manche du Violoncelle de manière que le pouce se trouve en jouant les premières positions du côté du manche à peu près vis-à-vis de l'index et du doigt du milieu; les doigts, en se courbant, tombent comme des marteaux sur les cordes. Le bras gauche conserve une tenue dégagée.

Les noms des parts du Violoncelle et de l'archet.

1. La table et en bas le fond.
2. L'éclisse.
3. Les F.
4. L'epine.
5. Le tire-cordes.
6. La touche.
7. Le manche.
8. Le sillet.
9. Les chevilles.
10. La caise des chevilles.
11. La coquille.
12. Le chevalet.
13. La baguette.
14. La pointe de l'archet.
15. La hausse de l'archet.
16. Les crins.

---

9. *Die Wirbel.*
10. *Der Wirbelkasten.*
11. *Die Schnecke.*
12. *Der Steg.*
13. *Die Bogenstange.*
14. *Der Kopf.*
15. *Der Frosch.*
16. *Die Haare.*

A ceux qui ont l'intention de s'instruire du développement de l'art de jouer du violoncelle, l'on peut recommander l'ouvrage: L'histoire du Violoncelle, par J. W. de Wasielewski:

Les éléments de la musique, exposés en peu de phrases nécessaires pour celui qui veut apprendre à jouer du Violoncelle.

Les cinq lignes de l'écriture de musique notée s'appellent le système de notes.

Les notes s'appellent dans la clef de Fa: 𝄢:

| on the lines:
Auf den Linien:
sur les lignes: | in the spaces:
in den Zwischenräumen:
dans les spaces intermédiaires: | under the lines:
unter den Linien:
au dessus des lignes: | over the lines:
über den Linien:
au dessous des lignes: |

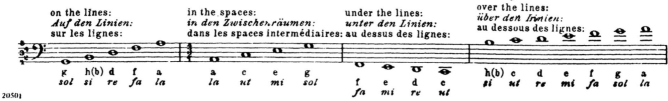

| g | h(b) | d | f | a | a | c | e | g | f | e | d | c | h(b) | c | d | e | f | g | a |
| sol | si | re | fa | la | la | ut | mi | sol | fa | mi | re | ut | si | ut | re | mi | fa | sol | la |

The seven natural tones are called:	*Die sieben natürlichen Töne heissen:*	Les sept tons naturels se nomment:

These tones can be raised with the sign ♯ by half a tone and will then be called: | *Dieselben können durch ein vorstehendes Zeichen ♯ (Kreuz) um einen halben Ton erhöht werden und heissen:* | Ces tons peuvent être haussés par le précédent signe ♯ (dièse) d'un demi ton, et dans ce cas, ils se nomment:

The tones can be lowered with the sign ♭ by half a tone and will be called: | *Durch das Zeichen ♭ (Be) werden die Töne um einen halben Ton erniedrigt und heissen:* | Par le signe bémol ♭ les tones sont baissés d'un demi ton et alors ils se nomment:

The double sharp (×) raises an interval one whole tone higher. | *Das Zeichen × (Doppelkreuz) erhöht die Noten noch um einen halben Ton mehr; z. B.* | Les doubles dièses (×) haussent les notes de tout un ton.

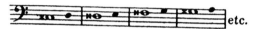 etc.

The double flat (♭♭) lowers an interval one whole tone. | *Das Doppelbe (♭♭) erniedrigt die Note um einen ganzen Ton.* | Les doubles bémols (♭♭) baissent les notes de tout un ton.

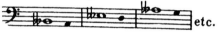 etc.

The ♮ is called the natural-sign. | *Das Auflösungs- oder Wiederherstellungszeichen ist ♮.* | Le signe ♮ se nomme un bécarre, qui replace la note.

The value of notes and rests: | *Der Wert der Noten und Pausen ist folgender:* | La valeur des notes et des pauses:

The dot prolongs the duration of the note or rest after which it is placed, one half in addition to its original value.
The second dot gives an additional quarter to the length of the original note. | *Der Punkt nach einer Note oder Pause verlängert dieselbe um die Hälfte ihres Wertes.* *Der Doppelpunkt verlängert die Note wieder um die Hälfte der Hälfte.* | Le point après une note ou pause les allonge de la moitié de sa valeur. Les deux points allongent les notes de nouveau de la moitié de la moitié.

Abbreviations. | *Abkürzungen in der Notenschrift.* | Abréviations.

20501

‖: :‖ Repetition sign.	‖: :‖ *Wiederholungszeichen.*	‖: :‖ Signe de répétition.
⌢ Sign of repose.(Halt.)	⌢ *Fermate, Halt- oder Ruhezeichen.*	⌢ fermate ou point de repos.

Scale.

The diatonic scale consists of 5 whole and two half tones.

The half tones of the major scale are between the 3. and 4. and the 7. and 8. interval.

The 6. and 7. interval of the minor scale is raised while ascending; the half tones are between the second and third and the seventh and eighth interval.

The major- and minor-triad consists of the 1. 3. and 5. tone of the scale; for instance.

Tonleiter.

Die diatonische Tonleiter besteht aus 5 ganzen und 2 halben Tönen.

In der Durtonleiter liegen die halben Töne zwischen der 3. zur 4. und 7. zur 8. Tonstufe.

In der Molltonleiter wird die 6. und 7. Tonstufe aufwärts erhöht und liegen die halben Töne zwischen der 2. zur 3. und 7. zur 8. Tonstufe.

Der Dur- und Molldreiklang besteht aus dem 1. 3. und 5. Ton der Tonleiter, z. B.

Gamme.

La gamme diatonique consiste de cinq entiers et de deux demi-tons.

Dans la gamme majeure les demi-tons sont entre le 3. et 4., et entre le 7. et 8. degré.

Dans la gamme mineure le 6. et 7. degré est élevé en haut et les demi-tons gisent entre le 2. et 3., et entre le 7. et 8. degré.

L'accord majeur et mineur consiste du 1. 3. et 5. ton de la gamme, p. e.

The keys.

There are 12 major and 12 minor-scales:
C major — A minor.
1♯
G „ — E „
2♯
D „ — B „
3♯
A „ — F sharp minor.
4♯
E „ — C „ „
5♯
B „ — G „ „
6♯
{F sharp major — D sharp minor.
6♭
{G flat major — E flat minor.
5♭
D „ „ — B „ „
4♭
A „ „ — F minor.
3♭
E „ „ — C „
2♭
B „ „ — G „
1♭
F „ „ — D „

The chromatic scale consists of half tones:

Tonarten.

Die 12 Dur- und 12 Molltonarten sind:
C dur — A moll.
1♯
G „ — E „
2♯
D „ — H „
3♯
A „ — Fis „
4♯
E „ — Cis „
5♯
H „ — Gis „
6♯
{Fis „ — Dis „
6♭
{Ges „ — Es „
5♭
Des „ — B „
4♭
As „ — F „
3♭
Es „ — C „
2♭
B „ — G „
1♭
F „ — D „

Die chromatische Tonleiter besteht aus halben Tönen:

Des tons.

On a 12 tons majeurs et 12 mineurs:
Ut majeur — La mineur.
1♯
Sol „ — Mi „
2♯
Re „ — Si „
3♯
La „ — Fa dièse mineur.
4♯
Mi „ — Ut „ „
5♯
Si „ — Sol „ „
6♯
{Fa dièse majeur — Re dièse mineur.
6♭
{Sol bémol majeur — Mi bémol mineur.
5♭
Re „ „ — Si „ „
4♭
La „ „ — Fa mineur.
3♭
Mi „ „ — Ut „
2♭
Si „ „ — Sol „
1♭
Fa majeur — Re „

La gamme chromatique consiste de demi-tons:

Enharmonic tones are: | *Enharmonische Töne sind:* | Tons enharmoniques:

-VI-

Time.

Time is indicated by means of figures placed at the commencement of a musical composition, designating the worth of the notes inside of a bar; for instance **C** = 4/4 or Common time standing for a whole measure; the other even measures consisting of 2/4, 6/8, 12/8, 2/2, 6/4 time and the odd measures of 3/4, 3/8, 9/8, 3/2, 5/4 time.

The natural accents of time of the **C** = 4/4 measure fall upon the 1. and 3. beats; of the 2/4, 3/4, 2/2, and 3/8 measure upon the first; of the 6/8, and 6/4 measure upon the first and fourth; of the 9/8 upon the first, fourth and seventh and of the 12/8 measure upon the first, fourth, seventh and tenth beat. The time is beaten in the following manner:

Vom Takt.

Die Taktart, die den Wert der Noten innerhalb eines Taktes angibt, steht zu Anfang des Tonstückes z. B. **C** = *4/4 oder ganzer Takt. Dann die anderen geraden Takte wie* 2/4 6/8 12/8 2/2 6/4 *und die ungeraden wie* 3/4 3/8 9/8 3/2 5/4 *etc.*

Der schwere Taktteil fällt im 4/4 = **C** *auf den 1. und 3. Taktteil, im* 2/4 3/4 2/2 3/8 *auf den ersten, im* 6/8 6/4 *auf den 1. und 4. im* 9/8 *auf den 1. 4. und 7. und im* 12/8 *Takt auf den 1. 4. 7. und 10. Taktteil. Der Takt wird gegeben:*

De la mesure

La mesure, qui indique la valeur des notes dans l'espace d'une barre de mesure, est écrite au commencement de la pièce, p. e. **C** = 4/4 ou mesure à quatre temps, alors les autres paires mesures comme 2/4 6/8 12/8 2/2 6/4 et les impaires comme 3/4 3/8 9/8 3/2 5/8 etc.

Le temps fort tombe dans la mesure à 4/4 = **C** sur la 1. et 3. part de mesure, dans la mesure à 2/4 3/4 2/2 3/8 sur la première, dans la mesure à 6/8 6/4 sur la première et quatrième, dans la mesure à 9/8 sur la 1. 4. et 7., et dans la mesure à 12/8 sur la 1. 4. 7. et 10. part de mesure. On bat la mesure ainsi:

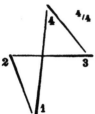 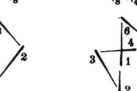

The clefs.

Three clefs are used for the Violoncello in accordance to the great tonal-compass of this instrument. They are herewith presented in the order as employed:

Von den Schlüsseln.

Bei dem Violoncell sind wegen des grossen Tonumfanges des Instrumentes drei Schlüssel gebräuchlich. Sie sind hier nach ihrem Einklang zusammengestellt.

Des clefs.

Pour le violoncelle on fait usage de trois clefs à cause du grand diapason de cet instrument. Elles sont exposées ici selon leur unisson.

The violin key or treble-clef of older notation must be played one octave lower, so that the first tone, for instance G, must be considered as open string.

Der Violinschlüssel nach älterer Art ist eine Oktave tiefer zu spielen, so dass hier der erste Ton (z. B.) G als leere Saite zu nehmen wäre.

La clef de sol de l'ancier ordre doit être jouée une octave plus basse, si que le premier ton, par exemple sol, doit être considéré comme la corde vide.

The positions

will be explained in detail in the second part of this school; the following is only a plain example of the positions most in use for beginning on the A and D strings.

Die Positionen

werden im 2. Heft dieser Schule eingehend behandelt; hier folgt nur ein kurzes Beispiel der Gebräuchlichsten für den Anfang auf der A und D Saite ohne Vorzeichen.

Les positions

seront expliquées en détail dans la deuxième partie; voici un exemple des positions les plus en usage pour commencer sur la première et deuxième corde.

In the fourth position the hand rests against the body of the instrument.

Harmonics are produced by touching the strings very lightly, without pressing them down.

In playing Harmonics, half of the string will produce the octave of the same.

One third, the fifth of the string in the second octave.

One fifth, the third of the string in the second octave.

The half of the half, the second octave of the string.

Pizzicato

Pizzicato is not produced by playing with the bow, but by pulling the string with the forefinger, of the right hand, while the thumb rests upon the side of the finger-board.

Bei der 4. Position setzt sich die Hand auf den Korpus des Instrumentes.

Flageolet wird hervorgebracht, indem der Finger die Saite ganz leicht berührt, ohne aufzudrücken.

Die Hälfte der Saite gibt im Flageolet die Oktave derselben.

Ein Drittel, eine Quinte der Saite in der 2. Oktave.

Ein Fünftel, eine Terze der Saite in der 2. Oktave.

Die Hälfte der Hälfte, die 2. Oktave der Saite.

Pizzicato

Die Bezeichnung pizzicato steht bei Stellen, welche nicht mit dem Bogen gestrichen, sondern mit dem Zeigefinger der rechten Hand angespielt werden, während der Daumen sich an die Seite des Griffbrettes setzt.

Dans la quatrième position la main se met sur le corps de l'instrument.

Les tons du Flageolet (harmoniques) sont produits en touchant la corde treslégèrement du doigt sans la presser.

Si l'on touche la moitié de la corde en Flageolet, le ton est celui de l'octave de la corde.

Si l'on en touche le tiers, le ton est celui de la quinte de la corde, dans la deuxième octave.

Si l'on en touche la quinte, le ton est celui de la tièrce de la corde dans la 2. octave.

Si l'on en touche la moitié de la moitié, le ton est celui de la 2. octave de la corde.

Pizzicato

Le nom „Pizzicato" est adopté à des passages, qui ne sont pas joués de l'archet, mais touchés de l'index de la main droite, durant que le pouce se met sur le côté du manche.

Thumb opposite 2,
Hand in C shape,
Lower fingers come
down @
same time

Signs and Abbreviations
Zeichen und Abkürzungen — Signes et Abréviations

⊓	Down bow	⊓	Herunterstrich	⊓	Tirez
V	Up bow	V	Hinaufstrich	V	Poussez
W.B.	Whole bow	W.B.	Ganzer Bogen	W.B.	Tout l'archet
U.H.	Upper half of bow	U.H.	Oberer halber Bogen	U.H.	Moitié supérieure de l'archet
L.H.	Lower half of bow	L.H.	Unterer halber Bogen	L.H.	Moitié inférieure de l'archet
N.	Nut of bow	N.	Frosch des Bogens	N.	Talon de l'archet
M.	Middle of bow	M.	Mitte des Bogens	M.	Milieu de l'archet
P.	Point of bow	P.	Spitze des Bogens	P.	Pointe de l'archet
⌐	Keep the fingers in position	⌐	Liegenlassen der Finger	⌐	Laissez les doigts en place

The Open Strings	Die leeren Saiten	Les Cordes à vide

open strings
wave (test w/ dc)

Bowing Exercises	Strich-Übungen	Exercices de l'archet

| First Position | Erste Lage | Première Position |
(Short stretch, minor third	(Kleine Spannung, kleine Terz)	(Petite Extension, Tierce mineure)
Finger - Exercises	Finger - Übungen	Exercices de doigts

W.B., U.H. & L.H.

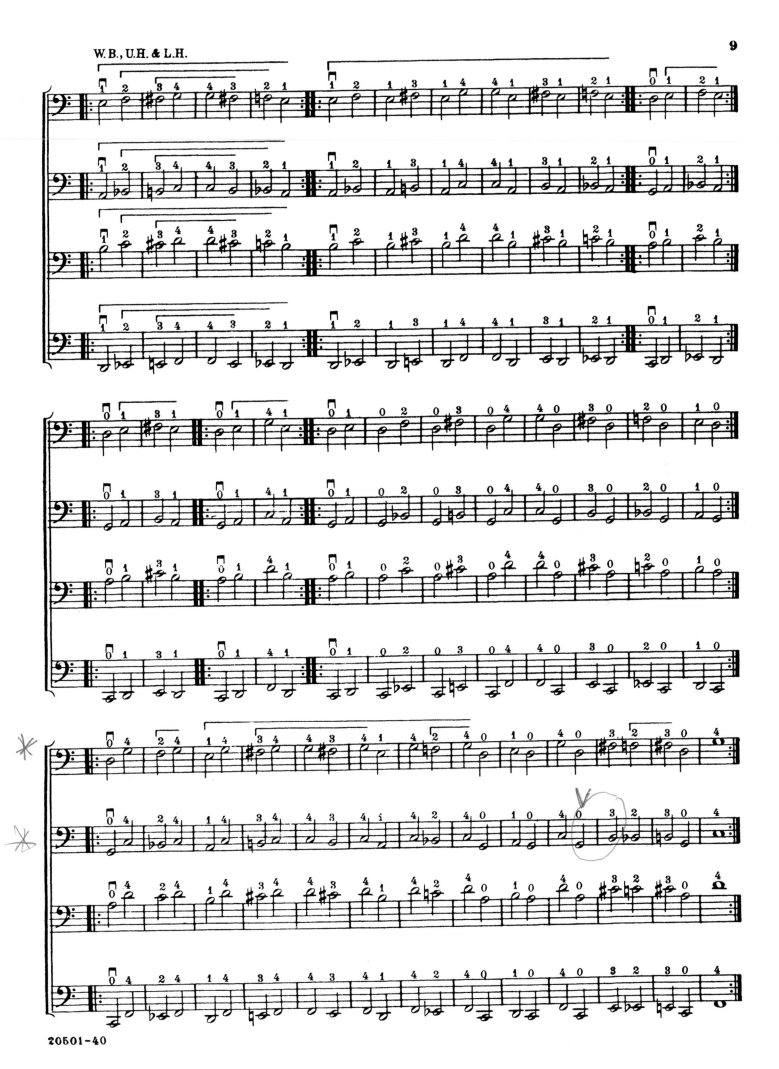

Notes of different values

All bowing exercises are also to be practised on all the strings.

Noten von ungleichem Werte

Sämtliche Strichübungen sind auch auf den anderen Saiten zu studieren.

Notes de valeurs inégales

Tous les exercices de l'archet à travailler sur toutes les cordes.

Smooth @ both ends of bowstroke. Don't lift. Don't twitch. Left hand more square, less reachy. Put all fingers down. Leave down. Arpeggios. Intervals, get to note from different strings

11

Exercises on 2 Strings
(Wrist)

Übungen auf 2 Saiten
(Handgelenk)

Exercices sur 2 Cordes
(Poignet)

Fifths
(Simultaneous placing of one Finger on 2 Strings)

Quinten
(einen Finger über 2 Saiten legen)

Quintes
(Poser un doigt sur 2 Cordes)

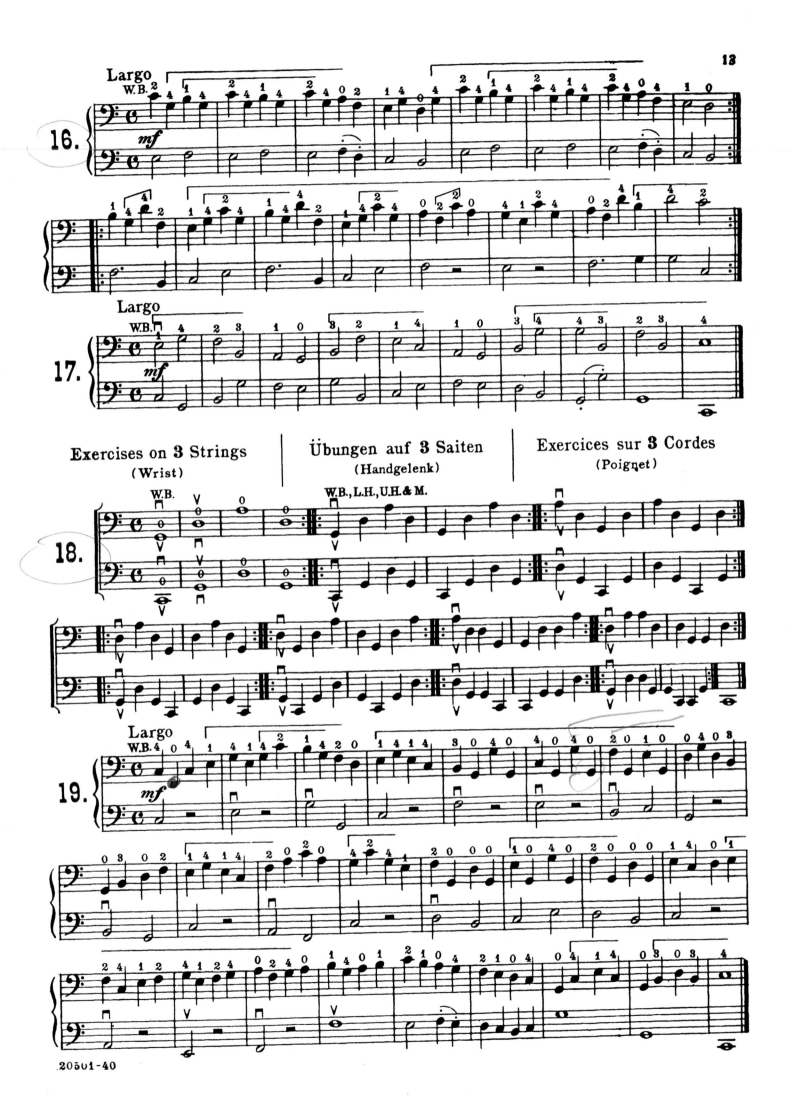

Exercises on **3** Strings
(Wrist)

Übungen auf **3** Saiten
(Handgelenk)

Exercices sur **3** Cordes
(Poignet)

Largo

20.

Exercises on 4 Strings | Übungen auf 4 Saiten | Exercices sur 4 Cordes
(Wrist) | (Handgelenk) | (Poignet)

21.

Scale of C major | C dur-Tonleiter | Gamme d'Ut majeur

CHORD—ACCORD

THIRDS — TERZEN — TIERCES

SIXTHS — SEXTEN — SIXTES

26.

OCTAVES — OKTAVEN

Lento

27.

Playing two Strings together | Anstreichen zweier Saiten | Doubles Cordes

Scale of G major | G dur-Tonleiter | Gamme de Sol majeur

28.

CHORD _ ACCORD

Tied Notes | **Gebundene Noten** | **Notes liées**
(Legato) | (Legato) | (Legato)

Wrist - Exercises | **Handgelenk-Übungen** | **Exercices du Poignet**

20501-40

On all **4** Strings, slowly at first, and gradually faster. | Auf allen **4** Saiten, erst langsam, dann schneller. | Sur les **4** Cordes, d'abord lente - ment, puis plus animé.

THIRDS — TERZEN — TIERCES

On all 4 String, slowly at first, and gradually faster | Auf allen 4 Saiten, erst langsam, dann schneller. | Sur les 4 Cordes, d'abord lente - ment puis plus animé

Wrist-Exercises | Handgelenk-Übungen | Exercices du Poignet

BARCAROLE

Allegretto

47

Double Stops | Doppelgriffe | Doubles Cordes

First Position | Erste Lage | Premiere Position
(Long stretch, major third) | (Grosse Spannung, grosse Terz) | (Grande Extension, Tierce majeure)

48

On the 4 Strings. Auf allen 4 Saiten. Sur les 4 Cordes

Scale of F major | F dur-Tonleiter | Gamme de Fa majeur

Chord Accord

Exercises on **2** Strings
On each pair of strings

Übungen auf **2** Saiten
Auf allen Saiten-Paaren

Exercices sur **2** Cordes
A travailler sur toutes les Cordes

Andante
W.B.

53.

mf

B flat major Scale | B dur-Tonleiter | Gamme de Si bémol majeur

W.B.

CHORD ACCORD

W.B.

54.

W.B.

| Moving the first finger a semitone, without changing the position of the thumb. | Hin-und Herrücken des ersten Fingers um einen halben Ton, ohne die Daumenlage zu verändern. | Glissement du premier doigt d'un demi-ton sans changer de position. |

Allegro moderato
W.B.

55.

mf

E flat major Scale   Es dur-Tonleiter   Gamme de Mi bémol majeur

Chord.— Accord

56.

Moderato (alla breve)

57.

Double Stops   Doppelgriffe   Doubles Cordes

Division of the Bow | Einteilung des Bogens | Division de l'archet

Short Bow (Wrist) | Kurzer Strich (Seitliche Handbewegung) | Coup d'archet bref (Poignet)

Andante con moto

On the 4 Strings.— Auf allen 4 Saiten.— Sur les 4 Cordes.

Long stretch, major third. The thumb moves a semitone higher | Grosse Spannung, grosse Terz. Der Daumen rückt um einen halben Ton höher | Grande extension, Tierce majeure. Glisser le pouce d'un demi-ton au-dessus

Scale of D major | D dur-Tonleiter | Gamme de Ré majeur

Chord - Accord

Andante

Thirds - Terzen - Tierces

A major Scale | A-Dur-Tonleiter | Gamme de La majeur

CHORD_ACCORD

73.

74.

75. Moderato

76. Allegro moderato

Different Bowings | Stricharten | Coups d'archet

Andante

77.

Double Stops | Doppelgriffe | Doubles Cordes

A Minor Scale | A moll -Tonleiter | Gamme de La mineur

Melodic — Melodisch — Mélodique

Harmonic — Harmonisch — Harmonique

Moving the fourth finger a semitone, without changing the position of the thumb. | Hin- und Herrücken des vierten Fingers um einen halben Ton, ohne die Daumenlage zu verändern. | Glissement du quatrième doigt d'un demi-ton sans changer de position.

E minor Scale | E moll-Tonleiter | Gamme di Mi mineur

Extended First Position

The first finger is stretched a semitone higher and placed beside the second.

Erhöhte erste Lage

Der erste Finger rückt bei grosser Spannung einen halben Ton höher, wird neben den zweiten gestellt.

Première Position avancée

Le premier doigt glisse d'un demiton plus haut, avec grande extension, pour se placer à côté du second.

Allegro moderato

85

Andante con moto

86

B minor Scale   H moll-Tonleiter   Gamme de Si mineur

Melodic — Melodisch — Mélodique

Harmonic — Harmonisch — Harmonique

CHORD - ACCORD

D minor Scale | D moll-Tonleiter | Gamme de Ré mineur

G Minor Scale   G moll-Tonleiter   Gamme de Sol mineur

Melodic — Melodisch — Mélodique

Harmonic — Harmonisch — Harmonique

CHORD — ACCORD

Moderato

Allegro moderato

92.

Contraction and extension of the fourth finger | Hin- und Herrücken des vierten Fingers bei grosser Spannung | Glissement du quatrième doigt dans les deux sens avec grande extension

93.

C minor Scale | C moll-Tonleiter | Gamme d'Ut mineur

Melodic._ Melodisch._ Mélodique

Harmonic._ Harmonisch._ Harmonique

42

Different Bowings | Stricharten | Coups d'archet.

Chromatic Scale | Chromatische Tonleiter | Gamme chromatique
(in the first position without alter- | (in erster Lage, ohne Veränderung der | (dans la première position, sans chan-
ing position of the thumb) | Daumenlage) | ger la position du pouce)

Technical Finger-Exercises
(On all **4** Strings)

Geläufigkeits-Übungen
(Auf allen **4** Saiten)

Exercices de Vélocité
(Sur les **4** Cordes)

98.

Allegro moderato

99.

On the **4** Strings — Auf allen **4** Saiten — Sur les **4** Cordes

Rhythmical Exercises | Rhythmische Übungen | Exercices de Rythme

The half Position

Hand and thumb to be placed a semitone from the nut; the second finger takes the former position of the first.

Die halbe Lage

Hand und Daumen rücken einen halben Ton nach dem Sattel, der zweite Finger nimmt die frühere Stelle des ersten Fingers ein.

La Demi - Position

Le premier doigt doit être placé à un demi-ton de la corde à vide, le deuxième prenant alors la place du premier.

On the 4 Strings — Auf allen 4 Saiten — Sur les 4 Cordes

Change of Positions | Lagen - Wechsel | Changements de Positions

Double Stops | Doppelgriffe | Doubles Cordes

List of the Principal Words used in Modern Music
With their Abbreviations and Explanations

A . . . . .to, in or at; *a tempo*, in time
Accelerando (accel.).Gradually increasing the speed
Accent . . . . . . .Emphasis on certain parts of the measure
Adagio . . . . . . .Slowly leisurely
Ad libitum (ad lib.).At pleasure; not in strict time
A due (a 2). . . . .To be played by both instruments
Agitato . . . . . .Restless, with agitation
Al or Alla. . . . .In the style of
Alla Marcia . . . .In the style of a March
Allegretto. . . . .Diminutive of allegro; moderately fast, lively; faster than *andante*; slower than *allegro*
Allegro . . . . . .Lively; brisk, rapid.
Allegro assai . . .Very rapidly
Amoroso . . . . . .Affectionately
Andante . . . . . .In moderately slow time
Andantino . . . . .Diminutive of *andante*; strictly *slower* than andante, but often used in the reverse sense
Anima, con }
Animato } . . .With animation
A piacere. . . . .At pleasure; equivalent to *ad libitum*
Appassionato. . . .Impassioned
Arpeggio . . . . .A broken chord
Assai . . . . . . .Very; *Allegro assai*, very rapidly
A tempo . . . . . .In the original tempo
Attacca . . . . . .Attack or begin what follows without pausing
Barcarolle . . . .A Venetian boatman's song
Bis . . . . .Twice, repeat the passage
Bravura . . . . . .Brilliant; bold; spirited
Brillante . . . . .Showy, sparkling, brilliant
Brio, con . . . . .With much spirit
Cadenza . . . . . .An elaborate, florid passage introduced as an embellishment
Cantabile. . . . .In a singing style
Canzonetta . . . .A short song or air
Capriccio a . . . .At pleasure, ad libitum
Cavatina . . . . .An air, shorter and simpler than the aria, and in one division, without Da Capo,
Chord. . . . . . . .The harmony of three or more tones of different pitch produced simultaneously
Coda . . . . . . .A supplement at the end of a composition
Col or con . . . .With
Crescendo (cresc.).Swelling; increasing in loudness
Da or dal . . . . .From
Da Capo (D. C.). .From the beginning
Dal Segno (D. S.). .From the sign
*Decrescendo(decresc.)*Decreasing in strength
Diminuendo (dim.).Gradually softer
Divisi. . . . . . .Divided, each part to be played by a separate instrument
Dolce (dol.) . . .Softly; sweetly
Dolcissimo . . . .Very sweetly and softly
Dominant. . . . . .The fifth tone in the major or minor scale
Duet or Duo . . . .A composition for two performers
E . . . . .And
Elegante . . . . .Elegant, graceful
Energico . . . . .With energy, vigorously
Enharmonic . . . .Alike in pitch, but different in notation
Espressivo . . . .With expression
Finale . . . . . .The concluding movement
Fine . . . . . . .The end
Forte (f) . . . . .Loud
Forte-piano (fp) .Accent strongly, diminishing instantly to piano
Fortissimo (ff) .Very loud
Forzando(fz>) . .Indicates that a note or chord is to be strongly accented
Forza . . . . . . .Force of tone
Fuoco, con . . . .With fire; with spirit
Giocoso. . . . . .Joyously, playfully
Giusto. . . . . . .Exact; in strict time
Grandioso. . . . .Grand; pompous; majestic
Grave . . . . . . .Very slow and solemn
Grazioso . . . . .Gracefully
Harmony. . . . . . .In general, a combination of tones, or chords, producing music
Key note . . . . . .The first degree of the scale, the tonic
Largamente . . . .Very broad in style
Larghetto. . . . .Slow, but not so slow as Largo; nearly like Andantino
Largo. . . . . . .Broad and slow; the slowest tempo-mark
Legato. . . . . . .Smoothly, the reverse of staccato
Ledger-line. . . . .A small added line above or below the staff
Lento . . . . . . .Slow, between Andante and Largo
L'istesso tempo. .In the same time, (or tempo)
Loco. . . . . . . .In place. Play as written, no longer, an octave higher or lower
Ma . . . . .But
Ma non troppo. . .Lively, but not too much so
Maestoso . . . . .Majestically; dignified
Maggiore . . . . .Major Key
Marcato. . . . . .Marked
Meno . . . . . . .Less
Meno mosso . . . .Less quickly
Mezzo. . . . . . .Half; moderately

Mezzo-piano (mp) .Moderately soft
Minore . . . . . .Minor Key
Moderato. . . . . .Moderately. *Allegro moderato*, moderately fast
Molto . . . . . . .Much; very
Morendo . . . . . .Dying away
Mosso. . . . . . .Equivalent to rapid. *Piu mosso*, quicker.
Moto . . . . . . .Motion. *Con moto*, with animation
Non. . . . . .Not
Notation . . . . . .The art of representing musical sounds by means of written characters
Obbligata . . . . .An indispensable part
Opus (Op.). . . . .A work.
Ossia . . . . . . .Or; or else. Generally indicating an easier method
Ottava (8va) . . .To be played an octave higher
Pause (⌢) . . . . .The sign indicating a pause or rest.
Perdendosi. . . . .Dying away gradually
Piacere, a . . . .At pleasure
Pianissimo (pp) .Very softly
Piano (p) . . . . .Softly
Più . . . . .More
Più Allegro . . . .More quickly
Più tosto. . . . .Quicker
Poco or un poco. .A little
Poco a poco. . . .Gradually, by degrees; little by little
Poco più mosso . .A little faster
Poco meno . . . . .A little slower
Poco più. . . . . .A little faster
Poi . . . . .Then; afterwards
Pomposo. . . . . .Pompous; grand
Prestissimo . . . .As quickly as possible
Presto . . . . . .Very quick; faster than *Allegro*
Primo (1mo). . . .The first
Quartet . . . . . .A piece of music for four performers.
Quasi. . . . . . .As if; in the style of
Quintet. . . . . . .A piece of music for five performers
*Rallentando (rall.)*Gradually slower
Replica. . . . . .Repetition. *Senza replica*, without repeats
Rinforzando . . . .With special emphasis
Ritardando (rit.) .Gradually slower and slower
Risoluto . . . . .Resolutely; bold; energetic
Ritenuto . . . . .In slower time
Scherzando. . . . .Playfully; sportively
Secondo (2do) . . .The second singer, instrumentalist or part
Segue. . . . . . .Follow on in similar style
Semplice . . . . .Simply; unaffectedly
Senza. . . . . . .Without. *Senza sordino* without mute
Sforzando (sf) . .Forcibly; with sudden emphasis
Simile or Simili .In like manner
*Smorzando (smorz)*Diminishing in sound. Equivalent to *Morendo*
Solo. . . . . . . .For one performer only. *Soli*; for all
Sordino . . . . . .A mute. *Con sordino*, with the mute
Sostenuto. . . . .Sustained; prolonged.
Sotto . . . . . . .Below; under. *Sotto voce*, in a subdued tone
Spirito. . . . . .Spirit. *con Spirito* with spirit
Staccato. . . . . .Detached; separate
Stentando . . . . .Dragging or retarding the tempo
Stretto or stretta.An increase of speed. *Piu stretto* faster
Subdominant . . . .The fourth tone in the diatonic scale
Syncopation . . . .Change of accent from a strong beat to a weak one.
Tacet. . . . . . ."Is silent" Signified that an instrument or vocal part, so marked, is omitted during the movement or number in question.
Tempo. . . . . . .Movement; rate of speed.
Tempo primo . . . .Return to the original tempo.
Tenuto (ten.) . . .Held for the full value.
Thema or Theme . .The subject or melody.
Tonic . . . . . . .The key-note of any scale.
Tranquillo . . . .Quietly.
*Tremolando, Tremolo*A tremulous fluctuation of tone.
Trio . . . . .A piece of music for three performers.
Triplet . . . . . .A group of three notes to be performed in the time of two of equal value in the regular rhythm.
Troppo . . . . . .Too; too much. *Allegro, ma non troppo*, not too quickly.
Tutti . . . . . . .All; all the instruments.
Un. . . . . .A, one, an.
Una corda . . . . .On one string.
Variatione . . . .The transformation of a melody by means of harmonic, rhythmic and melodic changes and embellishments
Veloce. . . . . . .Quick, rapid, swift.
Vibrato. . . . . .A wavering tone-effect, which should be sparingly used.
Vivace . . . . . .With vivacity; bright; spirited.
Vivo. . . . . . . .Lively; spirited.
Volti Subito V. S..Turn over quickly.

PRACTICE PLANNER

Date	Page	Goals/Comments	Remarks

Selected Solos for
CELLO

ADAGIO from "Toccata in C Major for Organ" .... Bach/Casals-Siloti B1946

ALLEGRO APPASSIONATO, Op. 43 .... Saint-Saens/Malkin B2717

ARIOSO from "Cantata No. 156" .... Bach/Isaac B2497

AT MORN (No. 2 from "Petits Morceaux") .... Squire B2936

AT TWILIGHT (No. 1 from "Petits Morceaux") .... Squire S4306

BOURRÉE, Op. 24 .... Squire B2518

CAPRICCIO ....Piatigorsky/Foss O5043

CELLO CONCERT... Foss O4903

CSARDAS ....Monti/Seredy B2519

CYGNE, LE (The Swan) ....Saint-Saens B2789

DANSE RUSTIQUE, Op. 20, No. 5 .... Squire B2517

FAIRY TALES (No. 5 from "Petits Morceaux") ....Squire/Buechner B2725

FORWARD, MARCH!, Op. 14, No. 6 .... Schlemeuller/Buechner B2630

GAVOTTE No. 2 in D Major, Op. 23 .... Popper B2709

IN DREAMLAND (No. 3 from "Petits Morceaux")..Squire/Buechner S4308

JEWISH SONG (No. 3 from "Jewish Life") ....Bloch/Kindler B1971

KOL NIDREI, Op. 47 ....Bruch/Lehmann B2713

LIEBESFREUD..Kreisler F1314

LIEBESLEID..Kreisler F1315

MEDITATION HEBRAIQUE ....Bloch/Kindler B1968

NIGUN (No. 2 from "Baal Shem").. Bloch B2772

PLAYERA (Spanish Dance No. 5) ....Granados/Munzer B2143

POMP AND CIRCUMSTANCE (Theme).. Elgar/Akers B3393

PRAYER (No. 1 from "Jewish Life")..Bloch/Kindler B1969

SCHÖN ROSMARIN ....Kreisler F1329

SONATA.. Webern O4860

STUDENT'S CONCERTO in D Major, Op. 213 .... Mendelssohn/Saenger L661

SUPPLICATION (No. 2 from "Jewish Life") ....Bloch/Kindler B1970

TARANTELLA, Op. 23.. Squire B2691

TWO PIECES .... Webern O4949